Maths

Bath · New York · Cologne · Melbourne · Delhi
Hong Kong · Shenzhen · Singapore

Helping your child

- The activities in this book will help your child to learn about maths. Pictures provide hints and clues to support your child's understanding.

- Your child will gain the confidence to: count to 20; add and take away; identify a range of 2D and 3D shapes; begin to tell the time; and order, group and measure objects.

- Your child will learn about numbers, shapes, halves, sets and pairs.

- Set aside time to do the activities together. Do a little at a time, so that your child enjoys learning.

- Give lots of encouragement and praise. Use the gold stars as rewards and incentives.

- The answers are on page 32.

This edition published by Parragon Books Ltd in 2017

Parragon Books Ltd
Chartist House
15-17 Trim Street
Bath BA1 1HA, UK
www.parragon.com

Copyright © Parragon Books Ltd 2009–2017

Written by Peter Patilla
Illustrated by Adam Linley
Cover illustrated by Simon Abbot
Educational Consultant: Christine Vaughan

ISBN 978-1-4748-7632-2

Printed in China

Contents

Write the numbers. Join each picture to the right number. Join each number to the right word.

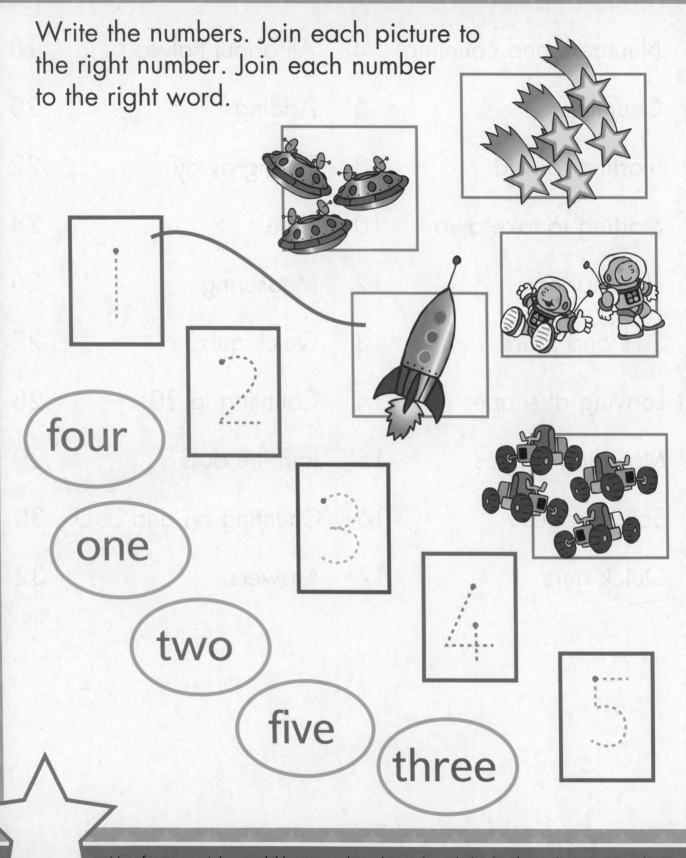

four

one

two

five

three

Note for parent: Ask your child to say each number and word aloud as he or she traces over them.

Note for parent: Help your child to work with numbers by saying a number and
asking them what number is one more/less.

5

Counting

Count the spots on each dog.
Write the number in the box.

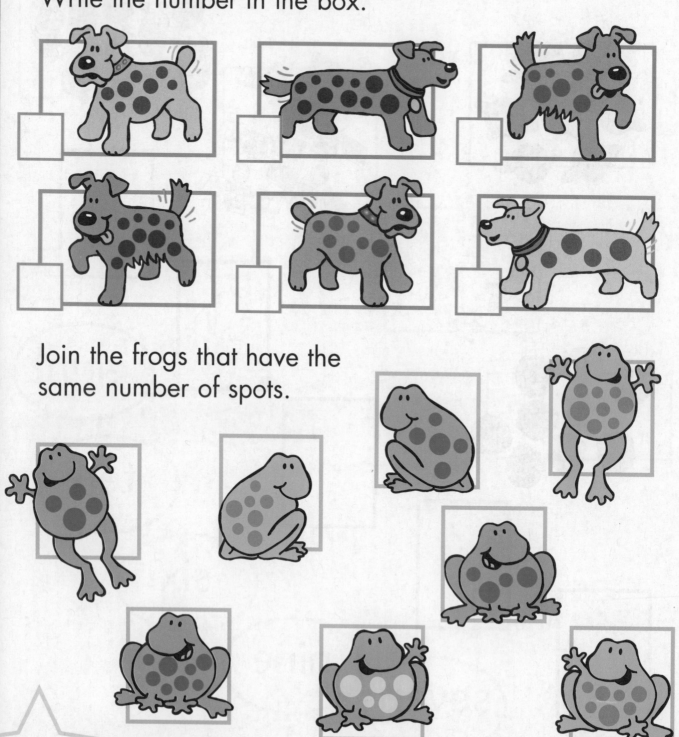

Join the frogs that have the
same number of spots.

Note for parent: This activity gives practice in using counting skills in different ways.

Each frog needs 10 spots.
Draw in the missing spots.

Join the pairs of dogs. Each pair must
have a total of 10 spots.

Note for parent: Help your child to write down all the pairs of numbers that add up to 10.

7

Write in the missing numbers.

 _____ **and** _____ **make** ☐ **altogether**

 _____ **and** _____ **make** ☐ **altogether**

 _____ **+** _____ **=** ☐   _____ **+** _____ **=** ☐

 _____ **+** _____ **=** ☐   _____ **+** _____ **=** ☐

Note for parent: In this activity your child is adding with objects, which helps to prepare them for adding with numbers.

Draw the missing socks above each arrow.

1 + 4 = 5

2 + 3 = 5

3 + 4 = 7

4 + 3 = 7

Write the missing numbers.

□ + 5 = 8

□ + 4 = 8

□ + 5 = 6

□ + 5 = 7

Dino the dinosaur eats 2 of everything he sees. Cross out how many pieces of food Dino eats. Write how many are left after Dino has eaten.

☐ take away **2**

leaves ☐

☐ take away **2**

leaves ☐

☐ take away **2**

leaves ☐

☐ take away **2**

leaves ☐

☐ take away **2**

leaves ☐

☐ take away **2**

leaves ☐

3 – 2 = ☐

2 – 2 = ☐

9 – 2 = ☐

10

How many fish has Charlie the cat eaten from each bowl? Join each START bowl to the correct FINISH bowl.

FINISH

START

take away **2**

take away **I**

take away **2**

take away **2**

take away **3**

take away **6**

Flat shapes

Cross the odd one out in each ring.

Tick all the shapes that are the same in each row.

Note for parent: Recognizing common shapes is a key part of maths teaching for your child at this age.

Join each set of shapes to its name.

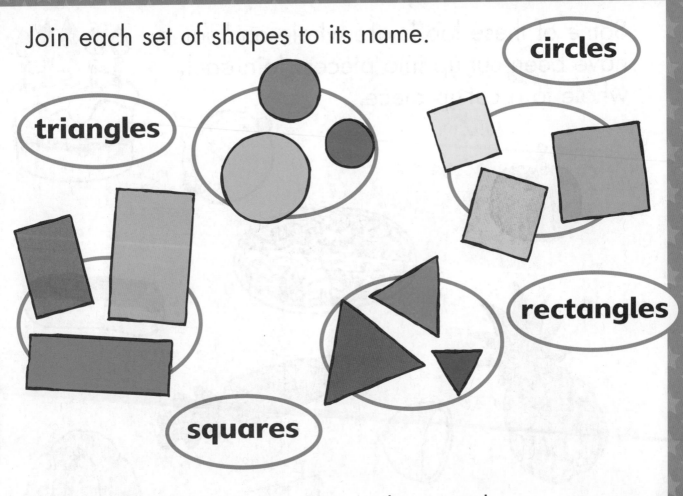

Draw a line to join the shapes that match.

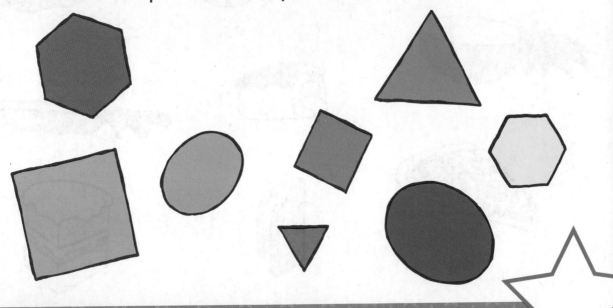

Note for parent: Gradually your child should learn the names of common shapes.

13

Looking at shapes

Some of these foods are whole and some have been cut up into pieces. Join each whole to a cut-up piece.

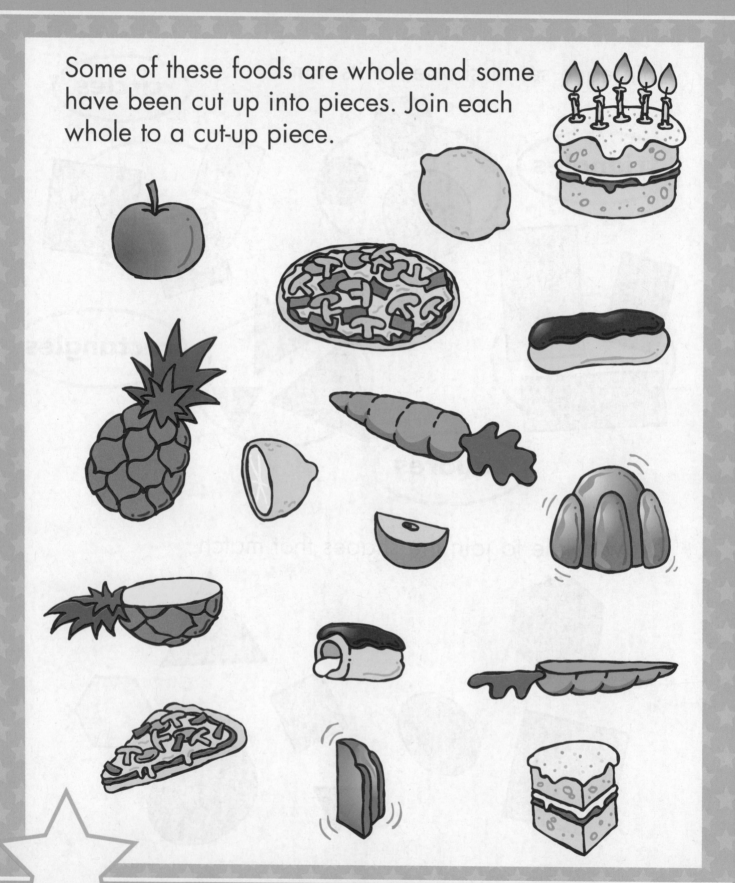

Matching shapes

Colour the matching shapes.

 colour red

 colour green

 colour blue

 colour orange

Note for parent: This activity gives further practice in examining shapes closely.

15

Solid shapes

Join each set of shapes to its name.

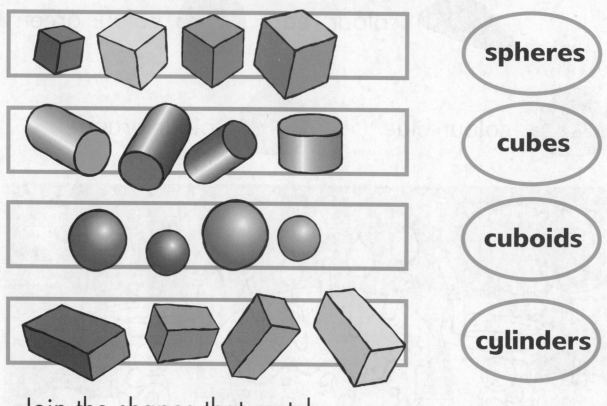

spheres

cubes

cuboids

cylinders

Join the shapes that match.

Note for parent: Ask your child to find examples of these solid shapes around the home. Ask them to recall the shape names as they become familiar to your child.

Join each START food to the correct FINISH food.

 START

add on **0**

 add on **3**

 add on **6**

 add on **6**

 FINISH

Join each START group to the correct FINISH group.

 START

take away **3**

 take away **2**

 take away **0**

 take away **5**

 FINISH

Note for parent: This activity helps your child to remember about adding and taking away.

17

All about halves

Colour half of each shape.

Draw the missing half of each shape.
Join the complete shape to its name.

triangle

circle

rectangle

square

Note for parent: Learning about half and fair shares is important in mathematics.

Colour half of the items in
each container.

Some marbles are put into two bags.
Put a tick (✔) if the sharing is fair.
Put a cross (✘) if the sharing is not fair.

Note for parent: Encourage your child to practise sharing real-life objects equally. Sweets
and coins of the same value are good examples to use.

19

Draw in the extra crayons.
Write the total number of crayons.

1 add **4**	**1 + 4 =**
3 add **3**	**3 + 3 =**
4 add **6**	**4 + 6 =**

There should be 10 cherries on each plate. Draw the missing cherries.

	4 + = 10
	8 + = 10

Note for parent: Your child may need to use the number track on page 21 to complete these additions.

Use the number track to help you.
Write how many beads are on each necklace.

4 + 3 =

6 + 2 =

2 + 5 =

3 + 3 =

1 + 5 =

6 + 3 =

Join the scarves that have the same total.

5 + 2

1 + 5

8 + 2

4 + 3

4 + 6

2 + 2

3 + 1

3 + 3

21

Taking away

Cross off the animals to be taken away.
Write how many are left.

4 take away **2**

$4 - 2 =$

7 take away **3**

$7 - 3 =$

8 take away **5**

$8 - 5 =$

Only 3 rockets are needed. Cross off the ones that have to be taken away. Write the answer.

$5 - \quad = 3$

$7 - \quad = 3$

Note for parent: Your child may need to use the number track on page 23 to complete these subtractions.

Use the number track to help you answer
the subtractions.

4 – 1 =

5 – 3 =

8 – 7 =

5 – 5 =

9 – 5 =

10 – 2 =

Join the stars that have the same answer.

10 – 5

8 – 7

5 – 0

10 – 7

6 – 3

6 – 5

23

Write in the missing numbers on the clock.

Write the times under each clock.

_____ o'clock

_____ o'clock

_____ o'clock

Look at the times. Draw in the missing hands.

half-past 3

half-past 8

half-past 12

Write the times under each clock.

half-past _____

half-past _____

half-past _____

Note for parent: For further practice with the concept of time, ask your child if they can name the days of the week and the months of the year.

25

Measuring

Draw a longer worm.

Draw a bigger flower.

Draw a taller rocket.

Draw a shorter lamp post.

Join up the pictures in order of size.
Start with the smallest.

Note for parent: In this activity your child is learning to estimate and compare measurements.

Quick quiz

Use the number track to help you write the answers.

0 1 2 3 4 5 6 7 8 9 10

$2 + 4 =$

$3 + 3 =$

$5 + 4 =$

$6 + 4 =$

$5 + 5 =$

$2 + 3 =$

$2 + 2 =$

$1 + 7 =$

$2 + 7 =$

$10 - 1 =$

$5 - 3 =$

$4 - 2 =$

$8 - 3 =$

$6 - 5 =$

$10 - 6 =$

$7 - 4 =$

$9 - 6 =$

$7 - 2 =$

Write in the missing numbers.

4 5 6 7 8

7 8 9 10

17 18 19 20

Join each word to a number.

12

15

11

14

eleven   twenty

fourteen   sixteen

twelve   thirteen

fifteen   seventeen

16

20

17

13

Join the dots in order.
Can you name the mystery animals?

Note for parent: This activity gives further practice in counting up to 20.

29

Counting on and back

Use the number track to help you count on.
Join each monster to its correct answer on the track.

$8 + 3$

$9 + 5$

$8 + 7$

$6 + 7$

$9 + 9$

$6 + 4$

0 1 2 3 4 5 6 7 8 9 10 11 12 13 14 15 16 17 18 19 20

$10 + 3$

$10 + 5$

$10 + 8$

$12 + 6$

$10 + 10$

$15 + 1$

Note for parent: This activity will help your child to use a number track to count on and back. Encourage your child to count on in twos and fives along the number track.

Use the number track to help you count back. Join each spaceship to its correct answer on the track.

0 1 2 3 4 5 6 7 8 9 10 11 12 13 14 15 16 17 18 19 20

Note for parent: Encourage your child to count back in twos and fives along the number track.

31

Answers

Page 6

8 spots, 10 spots, 6 spots, 9 spots, 7 spots, 4 spots.

Page 7

Clockwise from left: 10 + 0 = 10 spots, 7 + 3 = 10 spots, 9 + 1 = 10 spots, 6 + 4 = 10 spots, 5 + 5 = 10 spots, 8 + 2 = 10 spots, 4 + 6 = 10 spots.

Page 8

3 and 2 make 5 altogether, 2 and 4 make 6 altogether.
Buttons: 1 + 6 = 7; stars: 4 + 3 = 7; sweets: 5 + 2 = 7; hearts: 6 + 3 = 9.

Page 9

3 + 5 = 8, 4 + 4 = 8, 1 + 5 = 6, 2 + 5 = 7.

Page 10

Row 1: 4 take away 2 leaves 2, 6 take away 2 leaves 4, 5 take away 2 leaves 3; row 2: 8 take away 2 leaves 6, 7 take away 2 leaves 5, 10 take away 2 leaves 8; row 3: 3 – 2 = 1, 2 – 2 = 0, 9 – 2 = 7.

Page 11

Page 12

Page 13

Rectangles, triangles, circles, squares.

Page 14

Page 16

Row 1 – cubes, row 2 – cylinders, row 3 – spheres, row 4 – cuboids.

Page 17

Page 18

 triangle, circle,
 rectangle, square.

Page 19

Red bags = ✗; yellow bags = ✔.

Page 20

1 + 4 = 5, 3 + 3 = 6, 4 + 6 = 10.
4 + 6 = 10, 8 + 2 = 10.

Page 21

4 + 3 = 7, 2 + 5 = 7, 6 + 2 = 8, 3 + 3 = 6, 6 + 3 = 9, 1 + 5 = 6.
Total of 4: red and yellow scarves; total of 6: orange and dark-blue scarves; total of 7: pink and bright-blue scarves; total of 10: green and purple scarves.

Page 22

4 – 2 = 2, 7 – 3 = 4, 8 – 5 = 3, 5 – 2 = 3, 7 – 4 = 3.

Page 23

4 – 1 = 3, 5 – 3 = 2, 8 – 7 = 1, 5 – 5 = 0, 9 – 5 = 4, 10 – 2 = 8.
10 – 5 and 5 – 0; 8 – 7 and 6 – 5; 10 – 7 and 6 – 3.

Page 24

11 o'clock, 8 o'clock, 5 o'clock.

Page 25

From left to right: half-past 4, half-past 10, half-past 7.

Page 26

Page 27

2 + 4 = 6, 3 + 3 = 6, 5 + 4 = 9, 6 + 4 = 10, 5 + 5 = 10, 2 + 3 = 5, 1 + 7 = 8, 2 + 7 = 9, 2 + 2 = 4.
10 – 1 = 9, 5 – 3 = 2, 4 – 2 = 2, 8 – 3 = 5, 7 – 4 = 3, 6 – 5 = 1, 10 – 6 = 4, 9 – 6 = 3, 7 – 2 = 5.

Page 28

Top train: 9, 10, 11, 12, 13, 14, 15, 16, 17. Middle train: 11, 12, 13, 14, 15, 16, 17, 18, 19, 20. Bottom train: 7, 8, 9, 10, 11, 12, 13, 14, 15, 16.
Eleven – 11, fourteen – 14, twelve – 12, fifteen – 15, twenty – 20, sixteen – 16, thirteen – 13, seventeen – 17.

Page 29

Clockwise from top left: rhinoceros, tiger, monkey, elephant.

Page 30

8 + 3 = 11, 9 + 5 = 14, 8 + 7 = 15, 6 + 7 = 13, 9 + 9 = 18, 6 + 4 = 10.
10 + 3 = 13, 10 + 5 = 15, 10 + 8 = 18, 12 + 6 = 18, 10 + 10 = 20, 15 + 1 = 16.

Page 31

12 – 8 = 4, 12 – 6 = 6, 13 – 4 = 9, 11 – 9 = 2, 16 – 8 = 8, 12 – 5 = 7.
20 – 4 = 16, 20 – 5 = 15, 20 – 6 = 14, 20 – 8 = 12, 20 – 2 = 18, 20 – 7 = 13.